THE OXFORD PIANO METHOD

DUETS WITH A DIFFERE

Pauline Hall

MUSIC DEPARTMENT

OXFORD
UNIVERSITY PRESS

Piano duets provide an ideal form of ensemble playing—they encourage listening, musical awareness, and give-and-take between players. Above all, they are fun. This varied collection of duets provides opportunities for an ensemble of teacher and pupil, or two pupils together. There are also a few pages of aural guessing games and keyboard dexterity experiments. To get a musical and satisfying performance of these pieces, the parts should be practised separately before being played together. They may be used for sight-reading by more advanced pupils.

P.H.

Oxford University Press, Great Clarendon Street, Oxford OX2 6DP, England

Oxford University Press Inc., 198 Madison Avenue, New York, NY 10016, USA

Oxford is a trade mark of Oxford University Press

Acknowledgements

Illustrations by John Taylor

Thanks are due to the following for permission to include copyright material:

Broekmans en van Poppel B.V., Amsterdam, for 'Allegro' from *Kathenka's Musiekboek* (J. Andriessen).

Forsyth Brothers Ltd., 126 Deansgate, Manchester M3 2GR, for 'Lullaby' from *Teacher and I* (H. Scull).

Oxford University Press, for 'Donkey Ride' and 'March of the Sea Urchins' from *Sea Pictures* (E. Wells).

CONTENTS

Secondo

Swing song

Pauline Hall

The ruined abbey

Pauline Hall

Primo

Swing song

Pauline Hall

Play this as smoothly as you can. Your hands stay in the same position throughout. 8va means play an octave higher, in this case with both hands.

The ruined abbey

Pauline Hall

Secondo

The Irish washerwoman

arr. Pauline Hall

Primo

The Irish washerwoman

arr. Pauline Hall

This jolly Irish jig needs to swing along at a good, brisk pace – but don't let it hurry. It will need slow practice at first to get it neat.

Listening games

You need:
Two players
A piano
Pencil and paper for scoring

1. Guess what?

(Only use the notes from middle C to the next C up:

)

1st player shuts eyes. (Don't cheat!)
2nd player plays middle C, followed by any other note.
1st player guesses the name of the note and plays it. If he gets it right he scores 1 point.
Players change places.
First to get 5 points wins.

2. Mixed doubles

1st player plays 2 notes together (it is better not to choose notes that are too far apart – not more than an octave.)
2nd player sings or hums the top note.
1st player plays the 2 notes again.
2nd player sings or hums the lower note.
Scoring: 1 point if the top note was right.
2 points if the lower note was right.
Change places. First to reach 10 points wins.

Royal procession

Pauline Hall

In this piece the duet parts are written one below the other. Primo uses both hands.
Secondo plays 4 notes only:

mp
2
5
f
2
3
4
5
3

Secondo

Donkey ride

Elsie Wells

Primo

Donkey ride

Elsie Wells

Secondo

Ghost walk

Pauline Hall

Primo

Ghost walk

Pauline Hall

Your right hand plays an octave higher.

Secondo

Lullaby

Harold Scull

Primo

Lullaby

Harold Scull

Play this very smoothly and gently.
Your hands stay over these 5 notes:

Your right hand plays an octave higher.

Black key lullaby

You can make up a duet of your own, using the black keys only.

Primo
Three things to remember:
(1) Don't let your tune jump about – keep it on nearby keys.
(2) Let it fit the words – think them as you play.
(3) Make it end on F♯ .

Shadows are falling,
Now it is night.
Moonlight is gleaming,
Silver and bright.
Sleep, baby softly,
Soon dawn will break.
When the bright sunshine
Tells you to wake.

Secondo

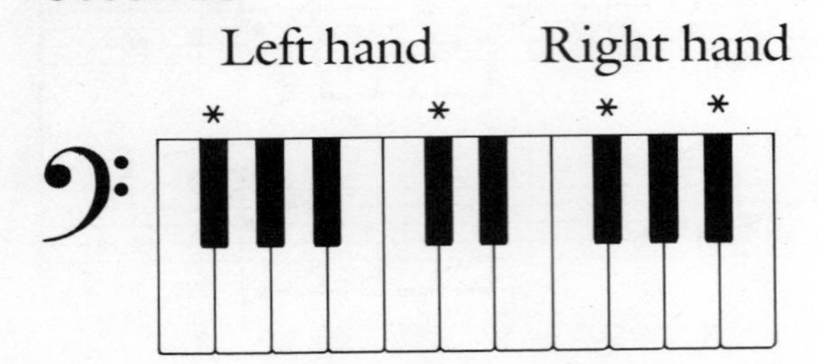

Play the 4* keys together as a chord.
Play your chord on the first word of each line to begin with. Experiment and see whether you can fit it in other ways.
Play quietly.

More games for good listeners

1. Chord quiz

1st player chooses one of these chords, and plays it.

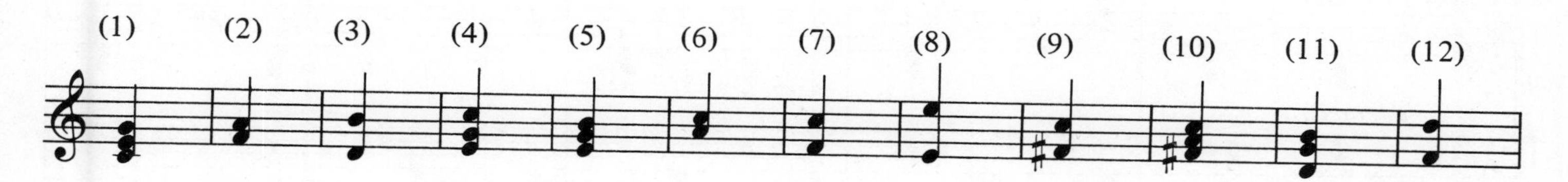

2nd player listens carefully, and says whether there are two or three notes in the chord.
Score 1 point for each correct guess.
Change places.

2. Copy Cat

Complicated to explain, but fun to play.
Rules
(1) You musn't look while the notes are being played by your opponent.
(2) The notes must be either next-door, or one away – like this:

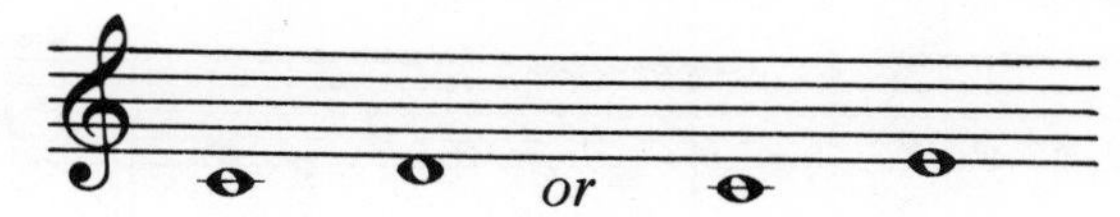

They can go up or down.
1st player – plays middle C and another note.
2nd player – plays these 2 notes and adds another.
1st player – plays these 3 notes and adds a fourth note.
2nd player – plays these and adds one.
The game goes on until someone forgets, and makes a mistake.
Score 1 point for each note you have added.

Secondo

Allegro

Jurriaan Andriessen

Primo

Allegro

Jurriaan Andriessen

Your hands stay over these notes:

Secondo

A Swiss tune

Herman Berens
(1826-1880)

Both hands play in the bass clef.

Tallis's canon

Listen to the tune as it starts in the treble – you come in with the same tune in bar 3 with the right hand. Your left hand plays the lower line.

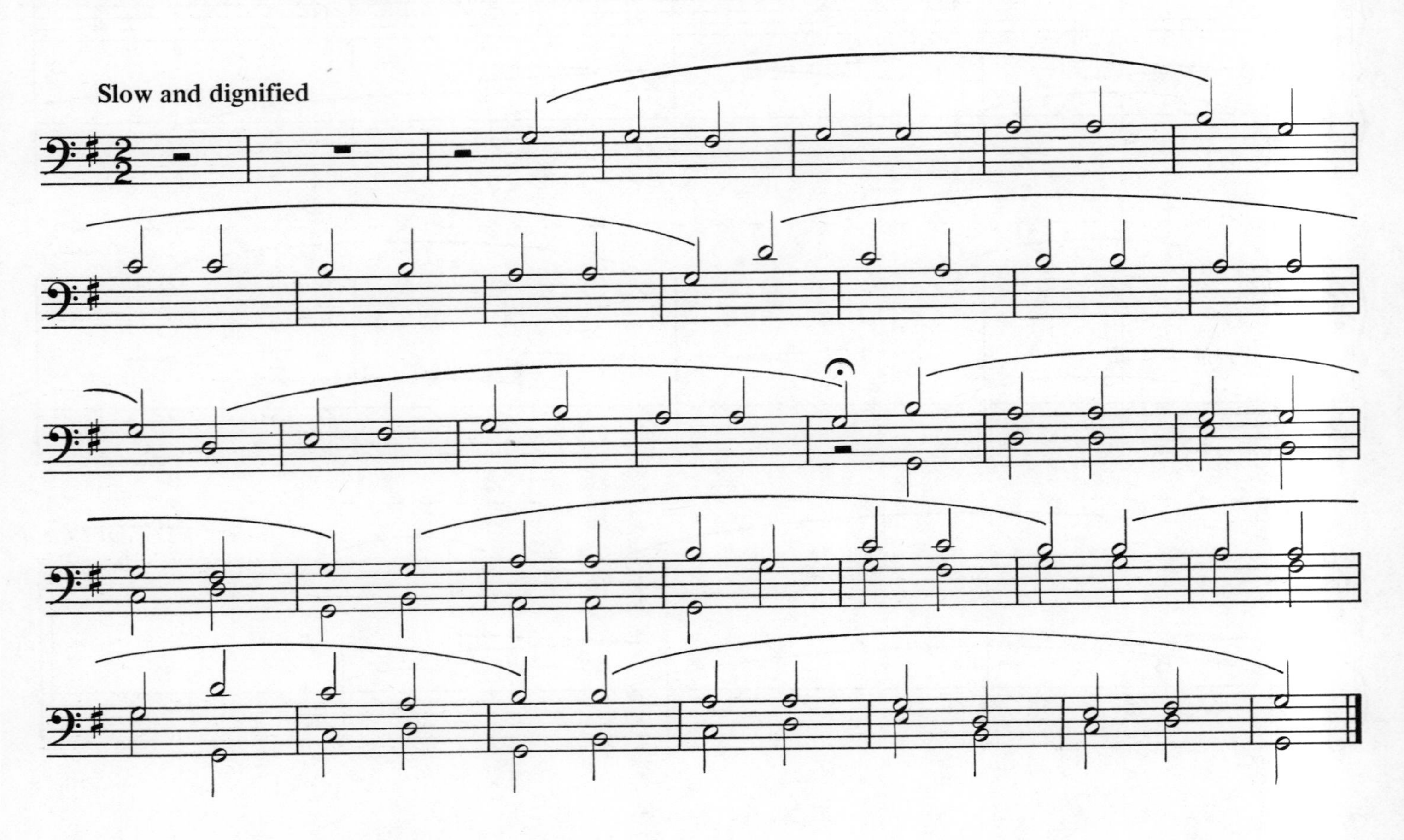

Primo

A Swiss tune

Herman Berens
(1826-1880)

Tallis's canon

A canon is a kind of round, with the same tune overlapping all the way through. Your left hand plays the lower line and the chords must be played *exactly* with the bass chords.
Thomas Tallis lived in the reign of Elizabeth I.

Secondo

March

Karl Wohlfahrt
(1874-1943)

Primo

March

Karl Wohlfahrt
(1874-1943)

Your hands stay over these notes:

Secondo

Happiness

Herman Berens

Primo

Happiness

Herman Berens

Your hands stay over these notes:

Secondo

Tricks for two

The first tune is quite easy – even so, you need to keep your wits about you.
Remember – there shouldn't be any breaks in the tune.

Twinkle, twinkle, little star

Bobby Shafto

Be warned – go slowly!

When you know what you are both doing –

Primo

Tricks for two

Here's something for two of you to try.
The trick is to sound as if only one person is playing. This means having your hand ready, and joining on at exactly the right time; and at the same time, keeping out of the other player's way. It helps to count out loud or to sing the words.

Twinkle, twinkle, little star

Bobby Shafto

Slow practice is essential!

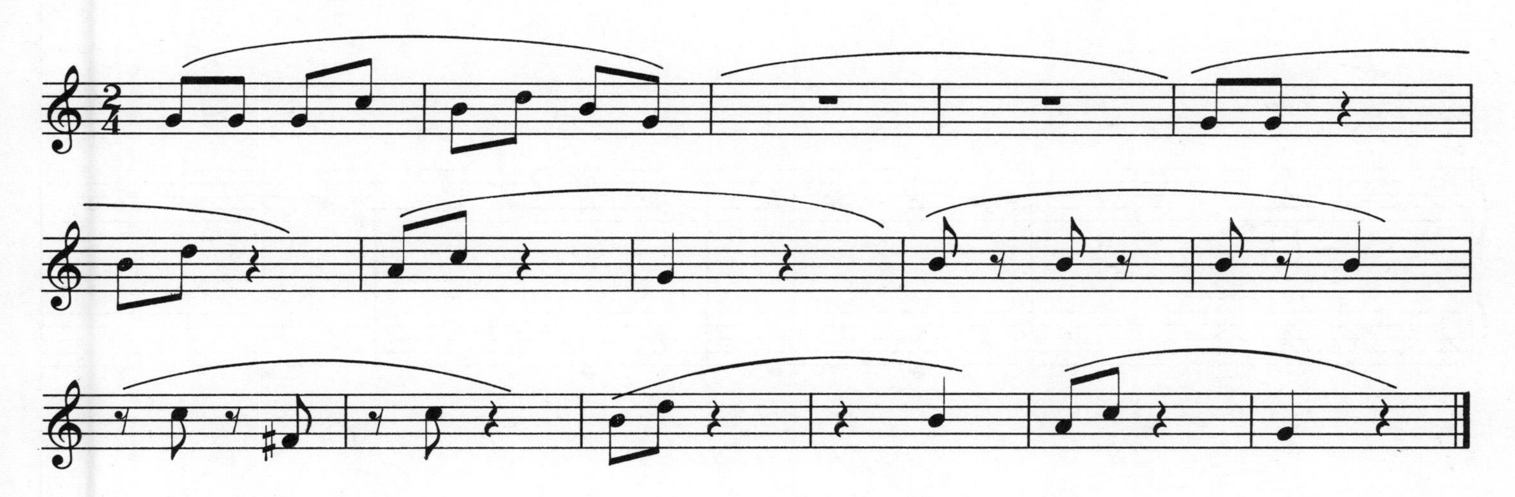

then is the time to play this *Presto* (quickly).

Secondo

March of the Sea Urchins

Elsie Wells

Primo

March of the Sea Urchins

Elsie Wells

Your left hand only plays 3 notes in this piece – F♯, G♯, A♯.
Your right hand plays 3 notes too – C♯, D♯, F♯.
All the keys are black.

Secondo

Berceuse

Adam Carse
(1878-1958)

Primo

Berceuse

Adam Carse
(1878-1958)

Andantino

8va

3

pp

3

8va

8va

mf

cresc.

poco rall.

8va

dim.

a tempo

8va

pp

8va

rall.

dim.

Reproduced and printed by
Halstan & Co. Ltd., Amersham, Bucks., England

the end